Karen lives with her family in the beautiful forest of Dean. She is originally from Bristol but moved from the city for a more rural setting.

She has spent many years working in primary schools, but now spends her days working as a quality control inspector in the engineering industry.

Karen loves walking, coffee with friends and all arts and crafts. But her highest priority is spending time with her family and dog. She loves nothing better than a break near the beach or strolling in the woods with her dog.

To Bertie,
♡
Karen Chaplin.

1

2

KAREN CHAPLIN

I AM DOG

AUSTIN MACAULEY PUBLISHERS™
LONDON * CAMBRIDGE * NEW YORK * SHARJAH

3

A CIP catalogue record for this title is available from the British Library.

ISBN 9781528980760 (Paperback)
ISBN 9781528989862 (ePub e book)

www.austinmacauley.com

First Published (2020)
Austin Macauley Publishers Ltd
25 Canada Square
Canary Wharf
London
E14 5LQ

Dedicated to John, Grace, Brandon, Troy and Coco.

5

6

Hello there, Dog.
Are you ready to play?
Your friends are around,
They're not far away.

They're waiting for you,
To show them the way.
And make the decisions,
"I am Dog!" you say.

With a wag and a woof,
Don't make them wait.
Just turn the page,
Go to page 8.

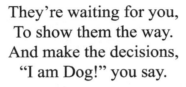

Alright then, Dog,
What are you doing today?
Have you got great plans?
Are you going far away?

You decide, Dog…
Go for a walk, page 9.
Go into the garden, page 11.
Is that your tummy rumbling? To eat, go to page 13.
Tired? Already? Go for a nap, page 28.

Great choice, Dog,
Where shall you go?
Garden or park?
Only you know.

All the adventures,
That this new day brings.
The sun is warm and shining,
And the birds like to sing.

But what about you,
What are you going to do?
You could sing with the birds,
If you really wanted to.

PARK

WALKIES

Where are you going to go Dog?
Go into the garden, page 11.
Go to the park, page 18.
Go to the funfair, page 23.
Or maybe you're feeling hungry?
Go for a snack, page 13.

9

You follow your nose,
To the hot dog stand.
The smells are so good,
Wafting over the land.

You eat up your hot dog.
The flavour is yummy.
The most perfect snack,
For a hungry dog's tummy.

What next, Dog?
Go on the dodgems, page 25.
Go on the funhouse, page 26.
Go on the big wheel, page 27.
Or,
Go home, page 8.
Go to the garden, page 11.
Go to the park, page 18.
Go home and take a nap, page 28.

10

Oh wow, Dog,
What a brilliant choice!
The smells are amazing,
And the grass is so moist.

The sun is so bright,
It's a beautiful day.
And all of your friends,
Have come out to play.

You play with your friends,
Hide and seek and then tag.
One by one they get tired,
By all the fun that they've had.

You decide to go off,
See what else you can do.
What other adventures'
Are waiting for you…

What next, Dog?
Go for a walk, page 9.
Go on a rocket ride, page 12.
Or,
Go home, page 8.
Go home and take a nap, page 28.

11

Wow, wow, wow,
What a cool rocket ship.
It's blue, red and white,
And black at the tip.

You climb aboard.
The steps are so tall.
Steady there, Dog!
You don't want to fall.

Sat in the seat,
Looking up at the sky.
Seat belt done up,
And ready to fly.

Where are you going to fly, Dog?
Fly to the Moon, page 14.
Fly to Jupiter, page 16.
Or, if you change your mind you could get off the rocket and…
Go home, page 8.
Go back into the garden, page 11.
Go to the park, page 18.

12

BYE, DOG

HAVE FUN!

Is that your tummy rumble?
Must be time for a snack!
You nibble on this,
You nibble on that.

Soon enough,
Your belly is full.
Can you hear that noise?
Is that your name they call?

Where now, Dog?
Go for a walk, page 9.
Go into the garden, page 11.
Go to the park, page 18.
Go for a nap, page 28.

13

You pressed the right buttons,
You arrived on the Moon!
Will you stay for a while?
Or, fly off pretty soon?

What do you think, Dog?
Stay on the Moon and explore, page 15.
Fly on to see Jupiter, page 16.
Or, fly back to the garden, page 11.

14

You decide to stay,
And explore some more.
The sky is so dark,
And you bounce on the floor.

The ground's a bit dusty,
And bumpy to walk.
Your voice sounds so funny,
So it's best not to talk.

You float and bounce,
And bumble around.
Picking up a small stone,
That you found on the ground.

You look back at the Earth.
It's so tiny and small.
From up on the Moon,
It's a long way to fall.

You float back to the ship.
It's so peaceful up here,
So calm and relaxed,
In this strange atmosphere.

You sit in your seat,
With your seatbelt all done.
And make a decision,
To fly off for more fun!

Where are you going now, Dog?
Fly off to see Jupiter, page 16.
Fly back to the garden, page 11.

15

The rocket slows down,
But doesn't quite stop.
It chugs through the clouds,
Like a frog going hop.

It's up to you, Dog!
You exploring some more?
Or have you decided,
This planet's a bore.

Explore Jupiter some more, it looks really cool, page 17.
Fly to the Moon, page 14.
Or, fly back to the garden, page 11.

16

This planet is AWESOME!
Though there's nowhere to land.
You can't see a surface,
No grass, mud or sand.

The clouds are so thick,
And they push you around.
For miles they stretch,
Yellow, white, red and brown.

After chugging along,
In your small rocket ship,
You decide it is time,
To conclude with your trip.

Where now, Dog?
Fly to the Moon, page 14.
Fly back to the garden, page 11.

17

The park is so lovely.
Has there been rain today?
You see some puddles,
Do you want to go play?

There's fishing at the lake,
Or a funfair just there,
Or maybe just stop,
And grab some fresh air.

What do you fancy doing, Dog?
Go fishing, page 19.
Go and play in the puddles, page 22.
Go to the funfair, page 23.
Or, if you've had enough of the park you could…
Go home, page 8.
Go to the garden, page 11.
Or,
Go home for a nap, page 28.

18

You settle down,
With a rod in your paw.
Peaceful and still,
Then a bird shouts out CAW!

You continue to fish,
For a while at least.
The fish that you catch,
You unhook and release.

Were the fish really hungry?
Did they take all the bait?
Was it loads that you caught?
Or did you just have to wait?

If you caught loads of fish turn to page 20.
If the fish weren't biting today turn to page 21.

19

CONGRATULATIONS, Dog!
You are good at this.
That last one was massive,
A whopper of a fish!

You think you caught 7,
You kind of lost count.
You were having such fun.
You forgot the amount.

Excellent fishing, Dog!
Where to next?
Go play in the puddles, page 22.
Go to the funfair, page 23.
Or, if you've had enough of the park you could…
Go home, page 8.
Go home and take a nap, page 28.

20

Never mind, Dog.
It wasn't your fault.
The fish didn't bite.
They don't want to be caught.

There's much more to do.
No time to feel sad.
Make another decision.
More fun to be had.

Where to now, Dog?
You could stay in the park and…
Go and play in the puddles, page 22.
Go to the funfair, page 23.
Or,
Go to the garden, page 11.
Go home, page 8.
Go and take a nap, page 28.

Splish, splash, splosh,
Puddles are the best.
There is no better way,
To put your wellies to the test!

Stamping and a stomping!
Splishing and a sploshing!
With water flying everywhere,
There is no sign of stopping.

You're getting pretty wet,
And decide you've had enough.
Your friends are all wet too,
But stopping is so tough.

You sit down on the grass,
And dry out before you say,
"What shall we do now?
What other games shall we play?"

You decide, Dog!
Go fishing, page 19.
Go to the funfair, page 23.
Leave the park and go back home, page 8.
Go to the garden, page 11.
Or are you tired from all the splashing?
Go home for a nap, page 28.

22

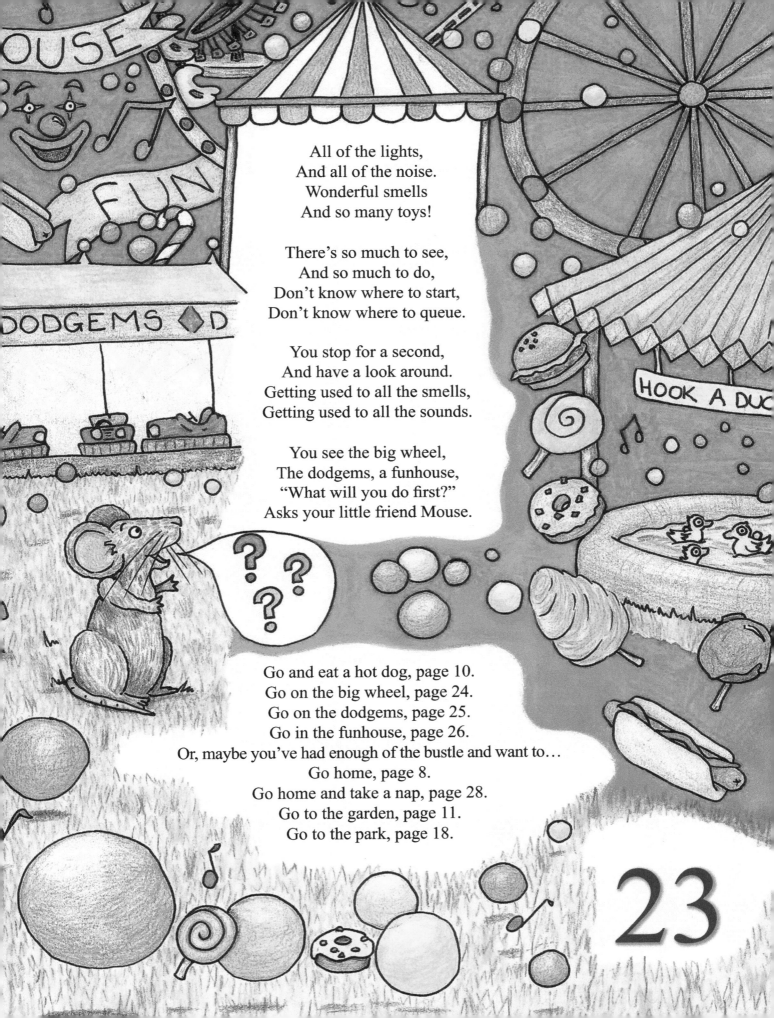

All of the lights,
And all of the noise.
Wonderful smells
And so many toys!

There's so much to see,
And so much to do,
Don't know where to start,
Don't know where to queue.

You stop for a second,
And have a look around.
Getting used to all the smells,
Getting used to all the sounds.

You see the big wheel,
The dodgems, a funhouse,
"What will you do first?"
Asks your little friend Mouse.

Go and eat a hot dog, page 10.
Go on the big wheel, page 24.
Go on the dodgems, page 25.
Go in the funhouse, page 26.
Or, maybe you've had enough of the bustle and want to…
Go home, page 8.
Go home and take a nap, page 28.
Go to the garden, page 11.
Go to the park, page 18.

23

"It's so big," you all say,
You can't see the top.
As this huge round machine,
Grinds and judders to a stop.

You get on with your friends,
Nice and calm, sitting still.
You can feel the excitement,
With the movement of the wheel.

As the wheel slowly turns,
You feel the air on your face.
Your ears start to flap,
As the wheel picks up pace.

It goes round several times,
And you look at the view.
The people look so tiny,
When they're underneath you.

After a while, the wheel slows,
Then it stops.
You feel sad when it's done,
It was great at the top.

Where to now, Dog?
Go and eat a hot dog, page 10.
Go on the dodgems, page 25.
Go to the funhouse, page 26.
Or, if you've had enough of the funfair, you could…
Go home, page 8.
Go to the garden, page 11.
Go to the park, page 18.
Go home and take a nap, page 28.

24

You wait for a token,
Then go find your car.
You decide on a red one,
It's the best one by far!

A loud horn buzzes,
The little car shakes.
You push down the peddle,
And off your car takes.

Bashing and bumping,
Crashing and clunking,
Spinning in circles,
Twirling and thumping.

It's such great fun,
Whizzing around.
But then the fun's over,
When another horn sounds.

All the cars stop,
And you're asked to get out.
You climb out your car,
And then wander about.

Where to next, Dog?
Go and eat a hot dog, page 10.
Go on the big wheel, page 24.
Go to the funhouse, page 26.
Or, maybe you want a change of scenery,
Go home, page 8.
Go to the garden, page 11.
Go to the park, page 18.
Go home for a nap, page 28.

25

The stairs are all wonky,
They go up and down.
There are noises, bright colours,
Things spinning around.

You go up some steep stairs,
And into a room.
There are mirrors for walls,
And a strange screeching tune.

There's a bubble machine,
That blows a big bubble.
And a weird moving floor,
That makes you wibble and wobble.

After laughing so much,
And falling about.
The funhouse is over,
And your friends start to shout,

"What now, Dog?"
"What do you want to do?"
"You make the decisions!"
"It's all up to you."

What do you decide?
Go and eat a hot dog, page 10.
Go on the big wheel, page 24.
Go on the dodgems, page 25.
Or, would you rather…
Go home, page 8.
Go to the garden, page 11.
Go to the park, page 18.
Go home for a nap, page 28.

26

That hot dog was good,
And now the big wheel.
Up you go to the top,
But you start to feel ill.

A little bit queasy,
As you look down below.
Your eyes like the view,
But your belly thinks "No."

Belly makes an odd noise,
And you start to feel sick.
Hot dog and big wheel,
That's not a great mix.

Soon the ride stops,
And you've had enough.
You sit with your friends,
But your tummy feels rough.

You decide it's best to,
Go home, page 8.
Go home and take a nap, page 28.

Feeling sleepy, dear Dog?
Cosy down, nice and snug.
With a yawn and a stretch,
Feeling warm with a hug.

Your eyelids are heavy,
Your pillow so soft.
With another BIG YAAAAWN,
You're soon drifting off.

Sweet Dreams, Dog.

28